Charlie's Big Catch

EGMONT
We bring stories to life

First published in Great Britain 2013
This edition published 2015 by Egmont UK Limited,
The Yellow Building, 1 Nicholas Road,
London W11 4AN

HiT entertainment

ISBN 978 0 6035 7142 8
62096/1
Printed in China

One morning, Charlie was enjoying a peaceful nap on the sofa, when Bronwyn burst into the room.

"Time to get up, Charlie! I've got a list of chores that need doing," she said. "You can start by fixing the kitchen tap."

"That's a two-man job," yawned Charlie. "I'll have to wait until Sam can help me."

"I thought you might say that," smiled Bronwyn. She opened the front door and there was Fireman Sam, holding his toolbox!

The two brothers were soon hard at work.

"This is just like when we were kids!" said Charlie.

"We were a great team!" grinned Sam.

Suddenly, Fireman Sam's phone rang. He was needed at the Fire Station. "Sorry, Charlie. I've got to go," said Fireman Sam.

Charlie was disappointed. He didn't often get to spend time with Sam. Luckily, it was a nice sunny day – perfect for a spot of fishing!

But when Charlie arrived at the harbour, Bronwyn was waiting for him.

"Can you take the children out to sea for their sea life project?" she asked.

"Come on then, kids. It looks like I'm not going to get any peace today anyway," smiled Charlie.

When they were out at sea, Charlie turned off the engine of his boat. "We don't want to scare away the sea life," he said.

The children took it in turns to look through the binoculars.

"I can see a cormorant!" cried Norman.

Meanwhile, Fireman Sam had arrived at the Fire Station.

"Elvis is fitting Jupiter's new hose," said Officer Steele. "It looks like he may need some help."

Poor Elvis was all tangled up in the big hose!

"I think you might be right, Sir," laughed Fireman Sam.

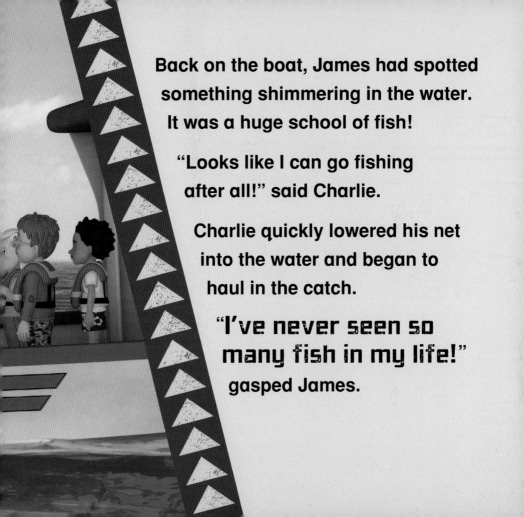

Back on the boat, James had spotted something shimmering in the water. It was a huge school of fish!

"Looks like I can go fishing after all!" said Charlie.

Charlie quickly lowered his net into the water and began to haul in the catch.

"I've never seen so many fish in my life!" gasped James.

Charlie winched in the net. "This is my biggest catch ever!" Charlie shouted out.

Suddenly, the winch motor began to whirr and stutter. Then it gave a loud **CLUNK** and stopped altogether.

"**Oh no!**" said Charlie. The net was so heavy, it was pulling the end of the boat into the sea!

Charlie pulled on the winch lever – but nothing happened. The winch was stuck!

"**Aargh! Help!**" cried the children, as the boat tipped further into the sea.

Charlie pulled out his mobile phone. "Don't worry," he told them. "We'll be fine. But I think it's time to call Fireman Sam!"

As soon as the call came in at the Fire Station, the team leapt into action.

"Come on, Elvis," said Fireman Sam. "There's no time to lose!"

The two firefighters jumped into Venus and headed for the lifeboat station. Within minutes, Neptune was zooming to the rescue with Fireman Sam at the helm.

The children spotted Neptune racing across the sea.

"Yay!" they cried. "It's Fireman Sam!"

"Are we glad to see you!" said Charlie, as Neptune pulled up next to the sinking boat.

It wasn't long before Fireman Sam and Elvis had everyone safely on board and the lifeboat was speeding back to shore.

"I wish I could have brought in those fish," said Charlie, back at the quay.

"We still can," smiled Fireman Sam.

Sam and Charlie sped back to the boat. They used buckets to drain the water, then they hauled in the fish. Everyone cheered from the quay!

"We should always work together!" said Charlie.

"Not if there's more fish involved," smiled Fireman Sam, holding his nose. "That's enough fish for one year!"

→ → → The End → → →